THE WAY OF THE CROSS

A PASSIONTIDE SEQUENCE OF WORDS AND MUSIC

COMPILED BY
DAVID OGDEN & PETER MOGER

RSCM

The Royal School of Church Music
19 The Close, Salisbury, Wiltshire, SP1 2EB, England
Tel: +44 (0)1722 424848 Fax: +44 (0)1722 424849
Email: press@rscm.com Website: www.rscm.com
Registered charity 312828

The Way of the Cross

Texts of the introduction, commentaries, music and graphic images are
copyright © 2007 The Royal School of Church Music,
except where otherwise attributed.

The prayers and service, from *Common Worship: Times and Seasons,* are
copyright © 2006 The Archbishops' Council, and used with permission.

First published 6 December 2007
re-printed December 2008

RSCM Order Code: S0124
RSCM Catalogue Number: RS36
ISBN: 978-0-85402-162-8

Cover design by Zednik Productions
Music and text origination by RSCM Press and MusicLines
Illustrations by Hilary Perona-Wright
Cover picture: The Kiss of Judas, Scenes from the Life of Christ (mosaic)
by Byzantine School, (6th century) Sant'Apollinare Nuovo, Ravenna, Italy
The Bridgeman Art Library
Printed in Great Britain by Halstan Group Ltd

Contents

Introduction

This sequence of words and music for Passiontide has at its root the visits of early Christian pilgrims to Jerusalem, who followed in the steps of Jesus from Pilate's house to Calvary, stopping along the route to make several 'stations' for prayer and reflection.

The stations featured here are drawn from the selection in *Common Worship: Times and Seasons*. They take the Passion narrative of the Gospel of Mark as a basis, adding a further passage from St John's Gospel.

A note on silence

Silence is a crucial feature of any reflection on the Passion of Jesus. A substantial period of silence should be kept after each of the readings and is advisable before each singing of the Trisagion. These silences, which are as important a part of the liturgy as the words and the music, provide windows through which we can begin to meditate upon the meaning of Our Lord's sacrifice.

The readings

The selection of stations presented here all have their root in the biblical story of Jesus rather than drawing on legend or popular, yet unscriptural, stories.

The music

Although *The Way of the Cross* is not a Passion play, the atmosphere created by the music is a vital part of the service. The effective contrast and interaction between drama and reflection can be achieved by introducing a wide range of musical textures, dynamics, tempi, and by varying the pace of each section.

The **Trisagion** serves as a musical thread throughout the service. Initially it can be sung freely by a solo voice at a distance. As voices and parts are added it gradually builds in dignity and intensity. Exaggerate the dynamics to achieve contrast. At each point, the first time is a reflection of what has just happened, the repeat looks forward to the next section.

The **hymns** do not have to be sung all the way through by everyone. Vary the textures in the verses to illustrate the words and feel free to designate one verse as a solo, ladies or men only or choir only. This should be indicated on the service sheet.

The **Psalms** are designed for choir singing although they could be sung by the whole congregation if appropriate. Vary the dynamics and texture of the accompaniment.

The **anthems** should be sung without fuss and as a continuation of the narrative. Some anthems may require all the singers while others could be sung by a smaller ensemble, perhaps in another part of the church.

Above all take time. The service is designed to be uncluttered with no announcements and plenty of space for reflection. It is advisable to have one reader for the scripture and one for the prayers.

Using the book

This book provides both a framework for a service and a repertory of texts and music. It can be used in the form in which it is presented in Part I (pages 1–46), with choral items selected from Part II (pages 47–95), or by substituting other musical settings or texts appropriate to the context of the worship. Where music is offered in Part II, page references are indicated in the main text. Where other music or texts may be used as substitutes, this is indicated in the margin by the sign ‡.

Performance notes are available on the website, where you can also find a text for the preparation of a congregational service leaflet.

Outline of the Service

The Gathering

I – Jesus in the garden of Gethsemane

II – Peter denies Jesus

III – Jesus before Pilate

IV – Jesus is led out to be crucified

V – Jesus is crucified

VI – Jesus dies on the cross

VII – The glory of the cross

The Conclusion

THE WAY OF THE CROSS

PART I: THE SERVICE

¶ THE GATHERING

The choir and ministers enter in silence

Trisagion 1 *

Music: David Ogden

Ho - ly God,___ Ho - ly and strong, Ho - ly and im - mor -
tal, Have mer - cy on us.   us.

voice over quiet organ music

Eternal God,
in the cross of Jesus
we see the cost of our sin
and the depth of your love:
in humble hope and fear
may we place at his feet
all that we have and all that we are,
through Jesus Christ our Lord. Amen.

Collect for Good Friday,
Common Worship: Additional Collects

Music: David Ogden

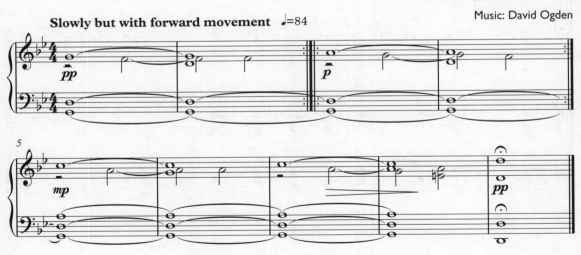

The organ music leads directly into the play-over for the hymn

*The Trisagion (Greek for 'thrice-holy') is an ancient trinitarian Christian hymn from the Eastern Orthodox Churches, where it is usually sung before the readings. In the West, the Trisagion has traditionally been associated with the Reproaches in the Good Friday Liturgy. The Church of England retains this association in Common Worship: Times and Seasons where it also appears as an optional ending to the Intercession on Palm Sunday, as well as being the concluding response to each of the prayers in The Way of the Cross.

Hymn: This is the night, dear friends, the night for weeping
HIGHWOOD 11 10 11 10

1   This is the night, dear friends, the night for weeping,
     when darkness' power overcomes the day,
     the night the faithful mourn the weight of evil
     whereby our sins the Son of Man betray.

2   This night the traitor, wolf within the sheepfold,
     betrays himself into his victim's will;
     the Lamb of God for sacrifice preparing,
     sin brings about the cure for sin's own ill.

3   This night Christ institutes his holy supper,
     blest food and drink for heart and soul and mind;
     this night injustice joins its hands to treason's,
     and buys for death the ransom of mankind.

4   This night the Lord by slaves shall be arrested,
     he who destroys our slavery to sin;
     accused of crime, to criminals be given,
     that judgement on the righteous judge begin.

5   O make us sharers, Saviour, of your passion,
     that we may share your glory that shall be;
     let us pass through these three dark nights of sorrow
     to Easter's laughter and its liberty.

Words: Richard Sturch b.1936
from the Latin of Peter Abélard 1079–1142
© 1990 Stainer & Bell Ltd. Used with permission
Music: R. R. Terry 1865–1938
© Oxford University Press. Used with permission

Hymn: This is the night, dear friends, the night for weeping

STRENGTH AND STAY 11 10 11 10

1   This is the night, dear friends, the night for weeping,
     when darkness' power overcomes the day,
     the night the faithful mourn the weight of evil
     whereby our sins the Son of Man betray.

2   This night the traitor, wolf within the sheepfold,
     betrays himself into his victim's will;
     the Lamb of God for sacrifice preparing,
     sin brings about the cure for sin's own ill.

3   This night Christ institutes his holy supper,
     blest food and drink for heart and soul and mind;
     this night injustice joins its hands to treason's,
     and buys for death the ransom of mankind.

4   This night the Lord by slaves shall be arrested,
     he who destroys our slavery to sin;
     accused of crime, to criminals be given,
     that judgement on the righteous judge begin.

5   O make us sharers, Saviour, of your passion,
     that we may share your glory that shall be;
     let us pass through these three dark nights of sorrow
     to Easter's laughter and its liberty.

Words: Richard Sturch b.1936
from the Latin of Peter Abélard 1079–1142
© 1990 Stainer & Bell Ltd. Used with permission
Tune: J. B. Dykes 1823–1876

¶   I – JESUS IN THE GARDEN OF GETHSEMANE

We adore you, O Christ, and we bless you,
All   **because by your holy cross you have redeemed the world.**

Reading

They went to a place called Gethsemane; and Jesus said to his disciples, 'Sit here while I pray.' He took with him Peter and James and John, and began to be distressed and agitated. And he said to them, 'I am deeply grieved, even to death; remain here, and keep awake.' And going a little farther, he threw himself on the ground and prayed that, if it were possible, the hour might pass from him. He said, 'Abba, Father, for you all things are possible; remove this cup from me; yet, not what I want, but what you want.'

Immediately, while he was still speaking, Judas, one of the twelve, arrived; and with him there was a crowd with swords and clubs, from the chief priests, the scribes, and the elders. Now the betrayer had given them a sign, saying, 'The one I will kiss is the man; arrest him and lead him away under guard.' So when he came, he went up to him at once and said, 'Rabbi!' and kissed him. Then they laid hands on him and arrested him.

Mark 14: 32–36, 43–46

Silence is kept

Psalm   ‡

either
Psalm 69: Anglican Chant (see next page)
or
Psalm 130: Out of the direst depths, John L. Bell (page 11)
or
Psalm 69: When the waters cover me, David Llewellyn Green (page 48)

Psalm 69: 1–13

Luke Flintoft

1   Save ' me, O ' God, ◆
     for the waters have come up, ' even ' to my ' neck.

2   I sink in deep mire where there ' is no ' foothold; ◆
     I have come into deep waters ' and the ' flood sweeps ' over me.

3   I have grown weary with crying; my ' throat is ' raw; ◆
     my eyes have failed from ' looking so ' long • for my ' God.

4   Those who hate me with- ' out a • -ny ' cause ◆
     are ' more than • the ' hairs of • my ' head;

5   Those who would des- ' troy me are ' mighty; ◆
     my enemies accuse me falsely:
           must I now give ' back • what I ' never ' stole?

6   O God, you ' know my ' foolishness, ◆
     and my ' faults • are not ' hidden ' from you.

7   Let not those who hope in you
           be put to shame through me, Lord ' God of ' hosts; ◆
     let not those who seek you be disgraced because of ' me,
           O ' God of ' Israel.

8,9 For your sake have I suffered reproach;
           shame has ' covered my ' face. ◆
     I have become a stranger to my kindred,
           an alien ' to my ' mother's ' children.

10   Zeal for your house has ' eaten me ' up; ◆
     the scorn of those who ' scorn you has ' fallen up- ' on me.

11   I humbled my- ' self with ' fasting, ◆
     but that was ' turned to ' my re ' proach.

12   I put on ' sackcloth ' also ◆
     and be- ' came a ' byword a ' mong them.

13   Those who sit at the gate ' murmur a- ' gainst me, ◆
     and the ' drunkards make ' songs a- ' bout me.

No Gloria

Psalm: Out of the direst depths

Words: from Psalm 130
paraphrase by John L. Bell

Music: from *The Psalmes in English Metre* 1579
arranged John L. Bell

Slowly

1. Out of the dir – est depths I make my deep – est plea. O
2. If you kept note of sins, be – fore you who could stand? But
4. Yes, with the Lord is grace and power to free and save. Re –

gra – cious – ly bow down your ear and lis – ten, Lord, for me.
since for – give – ness is your right, our rev – erence you com – mand.
–demp –tion from their ev – ery sin God's peo – ple yet shall have.

3. My soul longs for the Lord, and hopes to hear God's word. More

keen – ly than some watch for dawn, I wait and watch for God.

Prayer

Lord Jesus, you were betrayed by the kiss of a friend:
be with those who are betrayed and slandered and falsely accused.
You knew the experience of having your love
thrown back in your face for mere silver:
be with families which are torn apart by mistrust or temptation.
To you, Jesus, who offered your face to your betrayer,
be honour and glory with the Father and the Holy Spirit,
now and for ever.
Amen.

The choir sings

Trisagion 2

Music: David Ogden

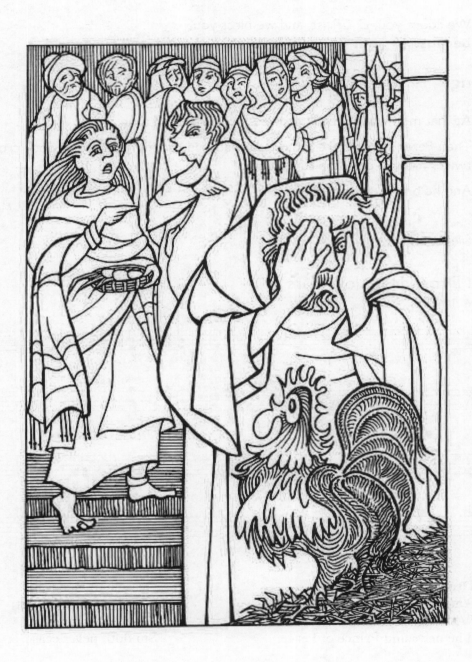

¶ II – PETER DENIES JESUS

We adore you, O Christ, and we bless you,

All   **because by your holy cross you have redeemed the world.**

Reading

At that moment the cock crowed for the second time.

Then Peter remembered that Jesus had said to him, 'Before the cock crows twice, you will deny me three times.'

And he broke down and wept.

Mark 14: 72

Silence is kept

Hymn: Drop, drop slow tears
SONG 46 10 10

1   Drop, drop slow tears,
    And bathe those beauteous feet,
    Which brought from heaven
    The news and Prince of Peace.

2   Cease not, wet eyes,
    His mercies to entreat;
    To cry for vengeance
    Sin doth never cease.

3   In your deep floods
    Drown all my faults and fears;
    Nor let his eye
    See sin, but through my tears.

Words: Phineas Fletcher 1582–1650
Music: Orlando Gibbons 1583–1625

Prayer

Lord Jesus, as Peter betrayed you,
you experienced the double agony
of love rejected and friendship denied:
be with those who know no friends and are rejected by society.
You understood the fear within Peter:
help us to understand the anxieties of those who fear for their future.
To you, Jesus, who gazed with sadness at his lost friend,
be honour and glory with the Father and the Holy Spirit,
now and for ever.
Amen.

The choir sings

Trisagion 3

Music: David Ogden

Unison voices 1st time men *p* 2nd time Full *f*

Ho - ly God,____ Ho - ly and strong, Ho - ly and im - mor - tal, Have mer - cy on us. us.

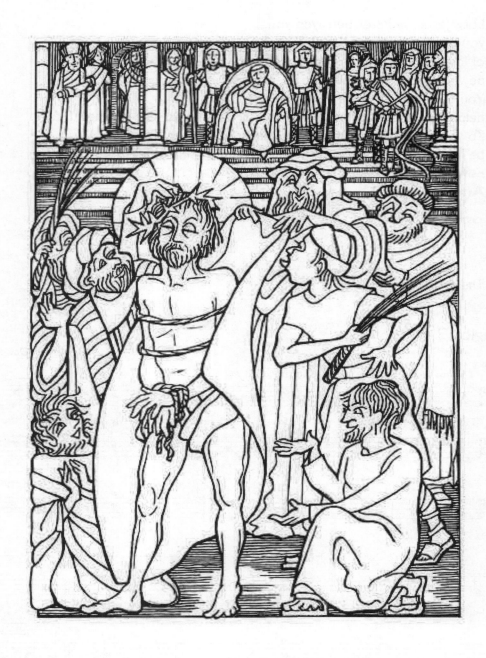

¶   III – JESUS BEFORE PILATE

We adore you, O Christ, and we bless you,

All   **because by your holy cross you have redeemed the world.**

Reading

Pilate asked them, 'Why, what evil has he done?' But they shouted all the more, 'Crucify him!' So Pilate, wishing to satisfy the crowd, released Barabbas for them; and after flogging Jesus, he handed him over to be crucified.

And they clothed him in a purple cloak; and after twisting some thorns into a crown, they put it on him. And they began saluting him, 'Hail, King of the Jews!' They struck his head with a reed, spat upon him, and knelt down in homage to him.

Mark 15: 14–15, 17–19

Silence is kept

Anthem   ‡

It is a thing most wonderful, Peter Moger (page 52)
or
It is a thing most wonderful, Philip Moore (page 58)

Prayer

Lord Jesus, you faced the torment of barbaric punishment
and mocking tongue:
be with those who cry out in physical agony and emotional distress.
You endured unbearable abuse:
be with those who face torture and mockery in our world today.
To you, Jesus, the King crowned with thorns,
be honour and glory with the Father and the Holy Spirit,
now and for ever.
Amen.

The choir sings

Trisagion 4

Unaccompanied SATB Choir.
1st time **f** 2nd time **p**

Music: David Ogden

Ho - ly God, _____ Ho - ly and strong, Ho - ly and im - mor -

- tal, _____ Have mer - cy on us.

us.

¶   IV – JESUS IS LED OUT TO BE CRUCIFIED

We adore you, O Christ, and we bless you,

All   **because by your holy cross you have redeemed the world.**

Reading

After mocking Jesus, they stripped him of the purple cloak and put his own clothes on him. Then they led him out to crucify him. They compelled a passer-by, who was coming in from the country, to carry his cross; it was Simon of Cyrene, the father of Alexander and Rufus.

Mark 15: 20–21

Silence is kept

Hymn *or* Anthem   ‡

either   Hymn: Take up thy cross (see over)
or   Anthem: Take up your cross, Ronald Corp (page 66)

Hymn: Take up thy cross, the Saviour said

BRESLAU LM

Last Verse Descant

5.To thee, great Lord the One in Three, all praise for ev-er-more as-cend:

O grant us in our home to see the life that knows no end.

1   Take up thy cross, the Saviour said,
     if thou wouldst my disciple be;
     deny thyself, the world forsake,
     and humbly follow after me.

2   Take up thy cross—let not its weight
     fill thy weak spirit with alarm:
     his strength shall bear thy spirit up,
     and brace thy heart, and nerve thine arm.

3   Take up thy cross then in his strength,
     and calmly every danger brave;
     'twill guide thee to a better home,
     and lead to victory o'er the grave.

4   Take up thy cross, and follow Christ,
     nor think till death to lay it down;
     for only he who bears the cross
     may hope to wear the glorious crown.

5   To thee, great Lord, the One in Three,
     all praise for evermore ascend:
     O grant us in our home to see
     the heavenly life that knows no end.

Words: C. W. Everest 1814–1877
Music: German traditional melody
harmony probably by W. H. Monk 1823–1889
descant: David Ogden

Prayer

Lord Jesus, you were worn down by fatigue:
be with those from whom life drains all energy.
You needed the help of a passing stranger:
give us the humility to receive aid from others.
To you, Jesus, weighed down with exhaustion and in need of help,
be honour and glory with the Father and the Holy Spirit,
now and for ever.
Amen.

The choir and congregation sing

Trisagion 5

Music: David Ogden

¶   V – JESUS IS CRUCIFIED

We adore you, O Christ, and we bless you,
All   **because by your holy cross you have redeemed the world.**

Reading

And they crucified him,
and divided his clothes among them,
casting lots to decide what each should take.

Mark 15: 24

Silence is kept

Anthem   ‡

Wondrous cross, Philip Wilby (page 70)
or
Crucifixus a 6, Antonio Lotti (page 78)

Prayer

Lord Jesus, you bled in pain as the nails were driven into your flesh:
transform through the mystery of your love
the pain of those who suffer.
To you, Jesus, our crucified Lord,
be honour and glory with the Father and the Holy Spirit,
now and for ever.
Amen.

The choir and congregation sing

Trisagion 6

Voices preferably unaccompanied
1st time *mp*, 2nd time *ff*

Music: David Ogden

DESCANT 1&2

Ho - ly God,____ Ho - ly and strong,

CONGREGATION

Ho - ly God,____ Ho - ly and strong,

SOPRANO ALTO

Ho - ly God, Ho - ly and strong,

TENOR BASS

ORGAN
optional

Ho - ly and im - mor - tal, Have mer - cy on us. us.

Ho - ly and im - mor - tal, Have mer - cy on us. us.

Ho - ly and im - mor - tal,____ have mer - cy on us. us.

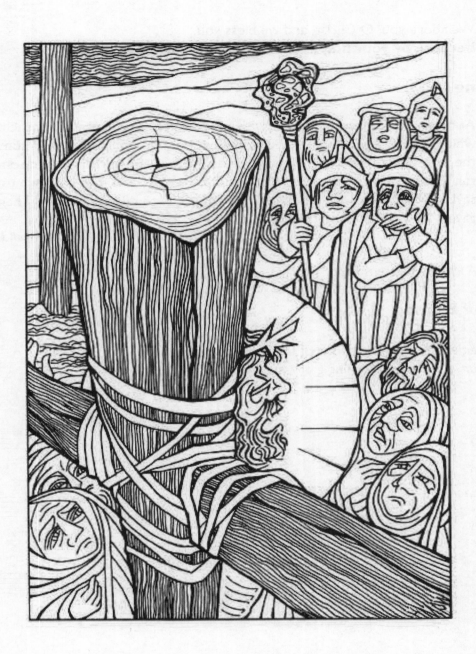

¶ VI – JESUS DIES ON THE CROSS

We adore you, O Christ, and we bless you,

All **because by your holy cross you have redeemed the world.**

Reading

At three o'clock Jesus cried out with a loud voice, 'Eloi, Eloi, lema sabachthani?' which means, 'My God, my God, why have you forsaken me?' When some of the bystanders heard it, they said, 'Listen, he is calling for Elijah.' And someone ran, filled a sponge with sour wine, put it on a stick, and gave it to him to drink, saying, 'Wait, let us see whether Elijah will come to take him down.' Then Jesus gave a loud cry and breathed his last.

Mark 15: 34–37

A lengthy silence is kept

Song *or* Hymn   ‡

either Song: At the foot of the cross (page 31)
or   Hymn: Morning glory, starlit sky (page 34)

Song: At the foot of the cross

Music and words: Derek Bond

left you   there_ for   dead._   And_ O what mer - cy I_
                                                      bow my knee_ be - fore

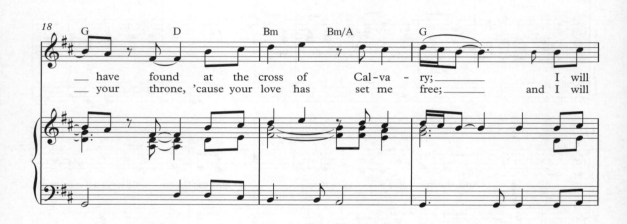

_ have   found   at   the cross   of   Cal-va - ry;_____   I will
_ your   throne, 'cause your love has   set me   free;_____   and I will

nev-er know your lone - li - ness, all_ on ac-count of me._   And I will
give my life_ to you,

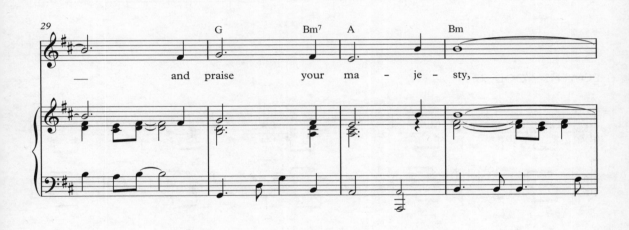

Alternative hymn

Hymn: Morning glory, starlit sky
SONG 13   77 77

BOWENS WOOD 77 77

1   Morning glory, starlit sky,
    leaves in springtime, swallows' flight,
    autumn gales, tremendous seas,
    sounds and scents of summer night;

2   soaring music, towering words,
    art's perfection, scholar's truth,
    joy supreme of human love,
    memory's treasure, grace of youth;

3   open, Lord, are these, thy gifts,
    gifts of love to mind and sense;
    hidden is love's agony,
    love's endeavour, love's expense.

4   Love that gives, gives evermore,
    gives with zeal, with eager hands,
    spares not, keeps not, all outpours,
    ventures all, its all expends.

5   Drained is love in making full;
    bound in setting others free;
    poor in making many rich;
    weak in giving power to be.

6   Therefore he who thee reveals
    hangs, O Father, on that Tree
    helpless; and the nails and thorns
    tells of what thy love must be.

7   Thou art God, no monarch thou,
    thron'd in easy state to reign;
    thou art God, whose arms of love
    aching, spent, the world sustain.

Words: W. H. Vanstone 1923-1999
© Mrs Isabella Shore,
c/o Mrs Helen Laughton, Northwood,
Sheffield Road, Hathersage, Hope Valley S32 1DA
Tune 1: Orlando Gibbons 1583–1625
Tune 2: Michael Fleming 1928–2006
© The English Hymnal Company Ltd
Used with permission

Prayer

Lord Jesus, you died on the cross
and entered the bleakest of all circumstances:
give courage to those who die at the hands of others.
In death you entered into the darkest place of all:
illumine our darkness with your glorious presence.
To you, Jesus, your lifeless body hanging on the tree of shame,
be honour and glory with the Father and the Holy Spirit,
now and for ever.
Amen.

Anthem   ‡

Were you there? arr. John Barnard (page 82)
or
Were you there? arr. David Ogden (page 86)

or

Hymn

O sacred head – Passion Chorale (page 90)

¶ VII – THE GLORY OF THE CROSS

We adore you, O Christ, and we bless you,

All   **because by your holy cross you have redeemed the world.**

All stand

Acclamation

Music: David Ogden

Praise to you O Christ, King of e-ter-nal glo-ry.

Christ humbled himself
and became obedient   un - to death,   even death   on   a   cross.

Therefore God has highly ex - al - ted him   and given him the
name that is above   ev - ery name.

Hear the Gospel of our Lord Jesus Christ according to John.

All   **Glory to you, O Lord.**

Reading

Jesus said to the crowd,

'The hour has come for the Son of Man to be glorified. Very truly, I tell you, unless a grain of wheat falls into the earth and dies, it remains just a single grain; but if it dies, it bears much fruit. Those who love their life lose it, and those who hate their life in this world will keep it for eternal life. Whoever serves me must follow me, and where I am, there will my servant be also. Whoever serves me, the Father will honour. Now my soul is troubled. And what should I say - "Father, save me from this hour"? No, it is for this reason that I have come to this hour. Father, glorify your name.' Then a voice came from heaven, 'I have glorified it, and I will glorify it again.' The crowd standing there heard it and said that it was thunder. Others said, 'An angel has spoken to him.' Jesus answered, 'This voice has come for your sake, not for mine. Now is the judgement of this world; now the ruler of this world will be driven out. And I, when I am lifted up from the earth, will draw all people to myself.'

John 12: 23–32

This is the Gospel of the Lord.

All   **Praise to you, O Christ.**

The congregation sits

Canticle: The song of Christ's glory   ‡

J. Harrison

1   Christ Jesus was in the ' form of ' God, ♦
     but he did not ' cling to e- ' quality with ' God.

2   He emptied himself, taking the form ' of a ' servant, ♦
     and was ' born in our ' human ' likeness.

3   Being found in human form he ' humbled him- ' self, ♦
     and became obedient unto death, ' even ' death on a ' cross.

J. Harrison

4   Therefore God has ' highly ex- ' alted him, ♦
     and bestowed on him the ' name above ' every ' name,

5   That at the name of Jesus, every ' knee should ' bow, ♦
     in heaven and on ' earth and ' under the ' earth;

6   And every tongue confess that Jesus ' Christ is ' Lord, ♦
     to the ' glory of ' God the ' Father.

Words: Philippians 2: 5–11

*An alternative setting of The song of Christ's glory by Grayston Ives
can be found on page 92.
Other alternatives might include:
Anerio or Bruckner: Christus factus est; Stainer: God so loved the world or
Moore: The song of Christ's glory*

Prayer

Most merciful God,
who by the death and resurrection of your Son Jesus Christ
delivered and saved the world:
grant that by faith in him who suffered on the cross
we may triumph in the power of his victory;
through Jesus Christ your Son our Lord,
who is alive and reigns with you,
in the unity of the Holy Spirit,
one God, now and for ever.
Amen.

Collect for the Fifth Sunday of Lent,
Common Worship

The choir and congregation stand and sing

Trisagion 7

Music: David Ogden

¶   THE CONCLUSION

Standing at the foot of the cross,
let us pray with confidence as our Saviour has taught us

Our Father, who art in heaven,
hallowed be thy name;
thy kingdom come;
thy will be done;
on earth as it is in heaven.
Give us this day our daily bread.
And forgive us our trespasses,
as we forgive those who trespass against us.
And lead us not into temptation;
but deliver us from evil.
For thine is the kingdom,
the power and the glory,
for ever and ever.
Amen.

Lord Jesus Christ,
Son of the living God,
set your passion, cross,
and death between your judgement and us,
now and at the hour of our death.
Give mercy and grace to the living,
rest to the faithful departed,
to your holy Church peace and concord,
and to us sinners eternal life and glory;
for you are alive and reign with the Father
and the Holy Spirit, one God, now and for ever.

All   **Amen.**

Hymn: My song is love unknown

LOVE UNKNOWN   66 66 44 44

Last Verse Descant

7. Here might I stay and sing:___ no sto-ry so di-vine;___

___ ne - ver was love, dear King, ne - ver was grief_____ like thine!

This is_____ my Friend in whose_____ sweet praise, I

all_____ my days could glad - ly spend.

1   My song is love unknown,
my Saviour's love to me,
love to the loveless shown,
that they might lovely be.
O who am I,
that for my sake
my Lord should take
frail flesh, and die?

2   He came from his blest throne,
salvation to bestow;
but men made strange, and none
the longed-for Christ would know.
But O, my Friend,
my Friend indeed,
who at my need
his life did spend.

3   Sometimes they strew his way,
and his sweet praises sing;
resounding all the day
hosannas to their King.
Then 'Crucify!'
is all their breath,
and for his death
they thirst and cry.

4 *   Why, what hath my Lord done?
What makes this rage and spite?
He made the lame to run,
he gave the blind their sight.
Sweet injuries!
yet they at these
themselves displease,
and 'gainst him rise.

5 *   They rise, and needs will have
my dear Lord made away;
a murderer they save,
the Prince of Life they slay.
Yet cheerful he
to suffering goes,
that he his foes
from thence might free.

6   In life, no house, no home
my Lord on earth might have;
in death, no friendly tomb
but what a stranger gave.
What may I say?
Heaven was his home;
but mine the tomb
wherein he lay.

7   Here might I stay and sing:
no story so divine;
never was love, dear King,
never was grief like thine!
This is my Friend,
in whose sweet praise
I all my days
could gladly spend.

Words: Samuel Crossman 1624–84
Music: John Ireland 1879–1962
© The John Ireland Trust,
20 Third Acre Rise, Oxford OX2 9DA
Descant: David Ogden

Blessing

May the Father,
who so loved the world that he gave his only Son,
bring you by faith to his eternal life.

All   **Amen.**

May Christ,
who accepted the cup of sacrifice in obedience to the Father's will,
keep you steadfast as you walk with him the way of his cross.

All   **Amen.**

May the Spirit,
who strengthens us to suffer with Christ that we may share his glory,
set your minds on life and peace.

All   **Amen.**

And the blessing of God almighty,
the Father, the Son and the Holy Spirit,
be among you and remain with you always.

All   **Amen.**

The ministers and choir depart in silence.

THE WAY OF THE CROSS

PART II: CHORAL RESOURCES

When the waters cover me

Salvum me

Words: from Psalm 69
Michael Perry

Music: David Llewellyn Green
arranged Noel Tredinnick

when   I   seek   what   can - not   be,   when _ my

friends   a - ban - don   me,   save   me,   O   God.

, poco rit.

Go back to page 12

It is a thing most wonderful

Words: William Walsham How

Music: Peter Moger

TENOR and BASS

And yet I know that it   is true;   he chose a poor and hum – ble lot.

and wept and toiled and mourned and died,   for   love   of those who

loved   him   not.

and I will love thee more,
love thee more   and more,   un – til   I   see thee

I   see thee   as   thou   art.
as   thou   art.

Go back to page 18

For Jonathan Bielby and the choir of Wakefield Cathedral

It is a thing most wonderful

Words: W. Walsham How 1823-97

Music: Philip Moore b.1943

York 17th August 1987

Go back to page 18

Take up your cross

Words and Music: Ronald Corp

1. I ac - know-ledge my
2. Hide your face from my

faults,   and my sin is___ e - ver be - fore me.
sins,   and___ blot out my wick-ed trans-gres - sions.

I ac-know-ledge my faults,_____ and my sin is_____ e-ver be-
Hide your face from my sins,_____ and__ blot out my wick-ed trans-

-fore me.   'Take up your cross',   the Sa-viour
-gres-sions.

said,_____ 'if you want to fol - low me,'   'Take up your

cross', the Sa - viour said,____ 'if you want to fol - low me'.

Go back to page 24

Wondrous cross

Words: Isaac Watts (1674-1748)

Music: Philip Wilby

all the vain things that charm me most,_____

all the vain things that charm me most,_____

SOPRANO
I sa - cri - fice_____ them. to_____ his

ALTO
I sa - cri - fice_____ them. to   his

TENOR
I sa - cri - fice_____ them. to   his

BASS
I sa - cri - fice_____ them. to   his

Go back to page 27

Crucifixus a 6

Music: Antonio Lotti

Go back to page 27

Were you there?

Words: African-American spiritual

Music: African-American spiritual
arranged John Barnard

Go back to page 38

Were you there?

Music: Traditional
arranged by David Ogden

© 2004 The Royal School of Church Music.

* The echo choir should be separated from the main choir and preferably out of sight of the listeners

Go back to page 38

Hymn: O sacred head

PASSION CHORALE 76 76 D

1   O sacred head, surrounded
     by crown of piercing thorn!
     O bleeding head, so wounded,
     so shamed and put to scorn!
     Death's pallid hue comes o'er thee,
     the glow of life decays;
     yet angel-hosts adore thee,
     and tremble as they gaze.

2   Thy comeliness and vigour
     is withered up and gone,
     and in thy wasted figure
     I see death drawing on.
     O agony and dying!
     O love to sinners free!
     Jesus, all grace supplying,
     turn thou thy face on me.

3   In this thy bitter Passion,
     Good Shepherd, think of me
     with thy most sweet compassion,
     unworthy though I be:
     beneath thy Cross abiding
     for ever would I rest,
     in thy dear love confiding,
     and with thy presence blest.

Words: Salve caput cruentatum,
14th-century Latin hymn
tr. H. W. Baker 1821–1877
Music: traditional secular melody
in H. L. Hassler's Musicalisches Lustgarten 1601
harmonised by J. S. Bach 1685–1750

Go back to page 38

A song of Christ's glory

Words: from Philippians 2
in the version from *Common Worship*

Music: Grayston Ives

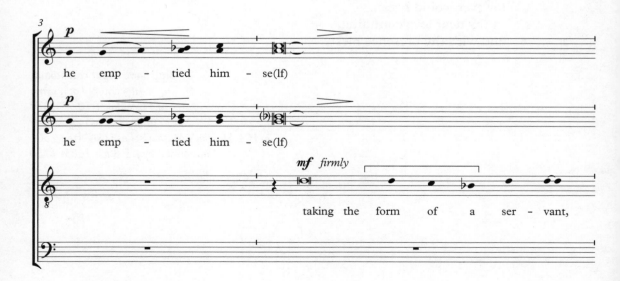

Christ Jesus was in the form_____ of Go(d)

Christ Jesus was in the form_____ of Go(d)

mf firmly
but he did not cling to e - qua - li - ty with God.

he emp - tied him - se(lf)

he emp - tied him - se(lf)

mf firmly
taking the form of a ser - vant,

and bestowed on him the name__ a - bove__ ev' - ry name.   That at the name of

That at the name of

That at the name of

That at the name of

Je - sus ev'-ry knee should bow;   in heaven and on earth and un - der the earth,

Je - sus ev'-ry knee should bow;   in heaven and on earth and un - der the earth,

Je - sus ev'-ry knee should bow;   in heaven and on earth and un - der the earth,

Je - sus ev'-ry knee should bow;   in heaven and on earth and un - der the earth,

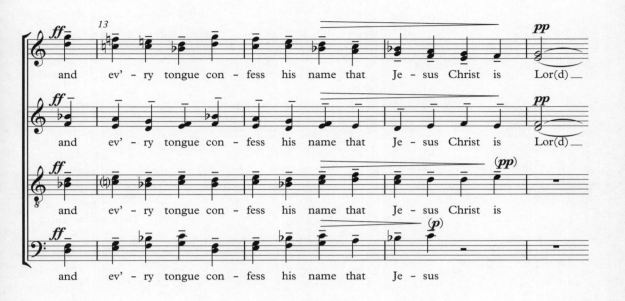

A version of this setting of the canticle for SATB choir and organ is available from www.rscm.com/wayofthecross

Go back to page 41